This book is lovingly dedicated to Whit and George
and to the child/grandchild on the way

Published by Peanut Butter Publishing
226 Second Avenue West
Seattle, WA 98119
(206) 281-5965
e-mail: pnutpub@aol.com
http://www.pbpublishing.com

Imagining the Animals / by Philippa Whitcomb;
Illustrated by Dorothea Bent.
Summary: By describing a "gift" that each animal brings, this beautiful
book offers an imaginative look at our fellow creatures and inspires a
deeper connection with the animal world. The thoughtful text and
lavish illustrations of this mother-daughter collaboration celebrate the
paradox of the unity and diversity of life on earth. This is a book that
will be enjoyed by all ages.
ISBN 0-89716-662-0
Library of Congress Catalog Number 96-070180

First Edition, 1997
Book designed by Rizwan Awan
The illustrations are done in Prismacolor pencils

10 9 8 7 6 5 4 3 2 1

Printed in Korea

IMAGINING
the
ANIMALS!

Written by Philippa Whitcomb
Illustrated by Dorothea Bent

Imagine the
Creation!
You see every
form unfold,
As each fish
and beast and bird
Assumes its pose.

You are dazzled
    by the brilliance,
You feel caught
    within a trance,
As each animal
    proclaims
Its Gift, its Dance.

The Eagle
    takes off skyward
With its Spirit
    tumbling down.

The Bear
begins a quest
To seek the Truth.

Our Pathfinder,
the Wolf,

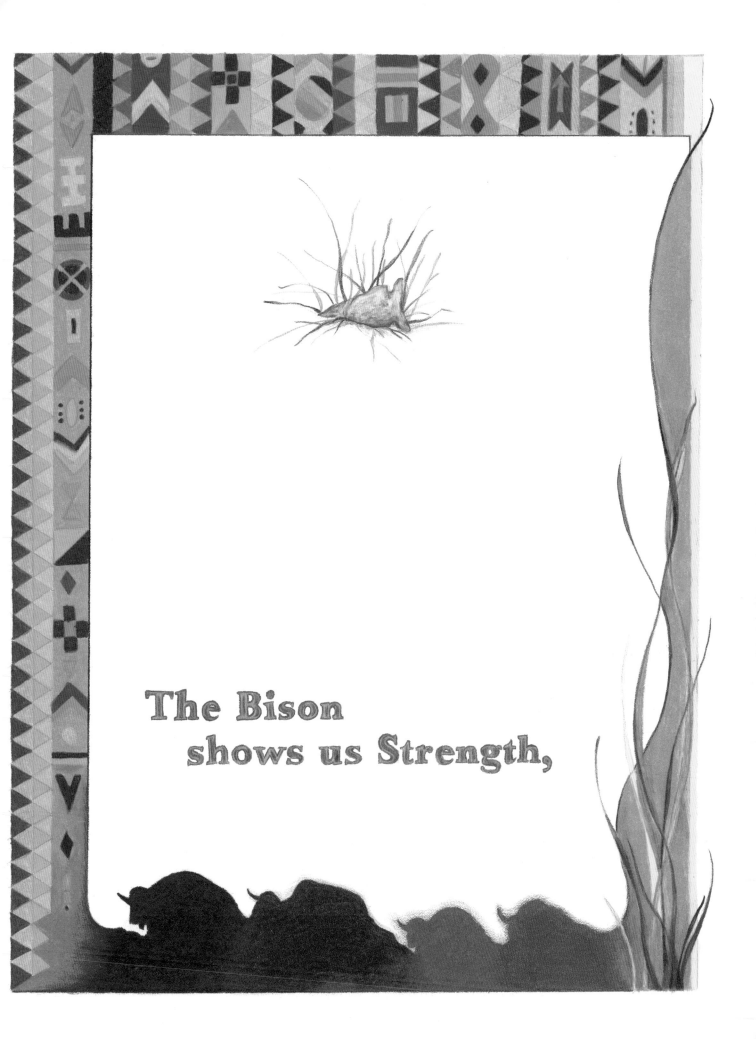

The Bison
        shows us Strength,

The Dolphin
sends the Energy
Of youth.

The Beaver
    teaches industry
And working
    toward a Goal.

The Spider
    sits and spins
A web of Fate.

The Snake
is a reminder
Of the cycle
of Rebirth,

The Lizard
signifies our
Dreaming state.

The Elephant,
Historian,

The Oyster
is our Hope,

The Hummingbird is Gladness Manifest.

From the Lion,
who is Leader,

And the Raven's
second Sight,

To the Mantis
saying Grace,
We all are blessed.

The diversity,
abundance,
The symphony
of sound,
The radiance
of color,

Life expressed!!!

IMAGINING the ANIMALS!

Imagine the Creation!
You see every form unfold,
As each fish and beast and bird
Assumes its pose.

You are dazzled by the brilliance,
You feel caught within a trance,
As each animal proclaims its Gift,
Its Dance.

The Eagle takes off skyward
With its Spirit tumbling down.

The Bear begins a quest
To seek the Truth.

Our Pathfinder, the Wolf,
The Bison shows us Strength,

The Dolphin sends the Energy
Of youth.

The Beaver teaches Industry
And working toward a goal;

The Spider sits and spins
A web of Fate.

The Snake is a reminder
Of the cycle of Rebirth,

The Lizard signifies
Our Dreaming state.

The Elephant, Historian,
The Oyster is our Hope,

The Hummingbird is Gladness
Manifest.

From the Lion, who is Leader,
And the Raven's Second Sight,

To the Mantis saying Grace,
We all are blessed.

The diversity, abundance,
The symphony of sound,
The radiance of color,
Life expressed!

That an **EAGLE** can see a rabbit on the ground from a mile up in the sky?

That a **POLAR BEAR** may wander for 250 miles in search of food?

That the howls of individual **WOLVES** are as varied as the singing voices of humans?

That the hump on a **BISON** is solid muscle that helps support its big head?

That **DOLPHINS** use their bodies to herd fish by doing a series of leaps, lunges and tailslaps?

That a **BEAVER** is a great swimmer partly because its nose and ears are provided with watertight valves?

That the silk of a **SPIDER** is produced as a fluid which solidifies on contact with the air?

That as a **SNAKE** sheds it turns its skin inside out?

That a **LIZARD** must spend time in a resting pose after activity because of poor blood circulation?

That the oldest wisest female **ELEPHANT** in the group is the leader, known as the matriarch?

That the pearl of the **OYSTER** is formed of nacre which is secreted in layers around a particle of foreign matter?

That the shoulder joint of a **HUMMINGBIRD** allows it to loop its wings backward and forward in a figure eight motion seventy times a second?

That at night, a **LION** can see six times better than a human can?

That a **RAVEN** can be taught to recognize numbers up to seven?

That a **MANTIS'** habit of swaying gently with its head raised and arms outstretched can mesmerize its prey?

DID YOU KNOW?